Dear Parents

As we all know, from an early age, the information our children learn about religion will later influence their beliefs, attitudes, and behaviors in later years.

This series tells about the birth, infancy, and childhood of Prophet Muhammad (peace and blessings be upon him), with stories and drawings that will appeal to our children and help them to understand. We hope and believe that you and your children will enjoy this series and find the stories not only entertaining, but informative as well.

2

LET IT RAIN

It was as if the clouds were playing hide-and-seek in the sky. They weren't anywhere to be seen over the plateau. Waiting patiently for a drop of rain, the purple violet took shelter in the shade of the date-palm. The drought lasted so long that the palm's trunk had begun to crack. The palm raised her fronds to the sky and prayed: "Oh Allah, please send us some rain." The withered wild-flower heard the whispered prayer, and solemnly said "Amen."

3

The violet said:
"My dear palm, let's pray together." Just at that moment a spotted butterfly alighted near the violet. She fanned out her wings and tried to comfort the flower with these words: "Friends! I have just heard this from Halima's flock. The people are gathering today to pray for rain. What do you say, shall we add our prayers to theirs?" The violet and the palm were very pleased to hear this news. Just then the people, with their drawn and pale faces, began to climb the hill to where the date-palm was standing.

5

It was clear that they were desperately in need of rain. They began to gather near the violet. They opened their hands:
"Allah, we are powerless and weak. We are in need of your aid. Please send us some rain," they prayed.

Everybody recited all the prayers they knew. But there was still not a cloud to be seen in the sky. The violet then noticed an old lady who was standing a little distance away. Nodding to her friends, the violet said: "Look, listen to what she is saying." As she continued, the plants and the butterfly started to listen: "There is a beautiful baby from Mecca in Halima's house. His name is Muhammad. He is different from all other babies. Maybe God will accept our prayers made in his name. Let's bring him here." The other people agreed that this was a good suggestion.

Halima was among the people who came to the hill to pray for rain. Upon the request of the old lady, Halima went straight home to fetch the Baby of Light. Halima held the rose-scented Baby of Light in her arms, bringing him to where the people had gathered.

The violet was very excited when she saw the Baby of Light in the arms of Halima. His scent was more beautiful than the scent of all the flowers. She knew that scent well; it was the scent of roses brought by the wind every morning, and now it was that which belonged to the Baby of Light. One of the people walked to the Baby of Light, took him into his arms and began to pray:

12

"Allah, who blesses us with plenty, please in the name of the Baby of Light send us some rain," he said. All the people there opened their hands and said "Amen."

At that moment, the violet noticed something else; there was a cloud hovering over the Baby of Light. The violet called to her friends, the date-palm and the butterfly: "Do you see the cloud over the Baby of Light? The cloud is getting bigger; it has nearly covered the sky. It is probably bringing us rain!"

The wild flower and the butterfly looked at the sky in hope. The people's hearts were racing with excitement. Suddenly they heard thunder. The rain drops started to drop, very slowly at first. All the flowers were smiling. The people were shouting with happiness "Hooray! Rain, it's raining! It's raining!"

As the rain began to dampen the wool of the lambs, they too began to smile and tried to catch the droplets on their tongues. They were baaing with delight. The date-palm and the violet smiled at one another through their wet leaves. The butterfly took shelter under the palm and used her fronds as an umbrella. She then watched the joy of all the creatures as the prayers made in the name of the Baby of Light were accepted by Allah.

Everyone knew that Allah
sent the rain because they
had the tenderhearted Baby
of Light among them.
They thanked Allah for the
wonderful baby. The love
they felt for the baby
increased even more;
Muhammad,
like the rain, brought love
and blessings wherever
he went.

Questions to think about:

1. Why were the creatures of the plateau sad?
2. What happened when Halima brought the Baby of Light to the hill-top?
3. In whose name did the people living on the plateau believe the rain had been sent?

Awaiting the Prophet

Hi there! I am a little violet who lives
in the countryside. I am really good friends
with the date tree and all the animals
who live on the plateau.
I want to share a story with you. At the time of
this story there was no rain on the plateau.
We were all praying to God for rain.
The people who lived near us came and
gathered here one day.
They started to pray for rain. They were
worried whether God would accept their
prayers or not.
Would the long drought soon end?
Do you wonder too?
Then come and share some moving
experiences with me in these pages.

Awaiting the Prophet Series

www.thelightpublishing.com

ISBN 978-1-59784-106-1

Awaiting the Prophet

The Sheltering Cloud

Nurefşan Çağlaroğlu

Published by The Light, Inc.
26 Worlds Fair Dr. Unit C
Somerset, New Jersey, 08873, USA
www.thelightpublishing.com

THE SHELTERING CLOUD
Awaiting the Prophet Series
-6-

Project Editor: Betül Ertekin
Translated from Turkish by: Jane Louise Kandur
English text edited by: Joshua D. Hendrick
Educational Consultants: Muhittin Küçük, Dr. F. Muharrem Yıldız
Illustrations: Süleyman Özkonuk
Graphic Design: Mustafa Kayan
Filming and Cover: SGSM

ISBN:
978-1-59784-109-2

SERIES ISBN:
978-1-59784-126-9

Printed by
Çağlayan A.Ş. Izmir, Turkey
Sarnıç Yolu Üzeri No:7 Gaziemir
Tel: (0 232) 252 22 85

May 2007